IT HAPPENED IN CANADA

Book 2

Stories of Canadians Who Made a Difference

IT HAPPENED IN CANADA

Book 2

Stories of Canadians
Who Made a Difference

BY
EMILY-JANE HILLS ORFORD

The cover photograph taken by the author,
Emily-Jane Hills Orford

Photograph of the author
was taken by Norman Alfred Hills.

Published by:

Baico Publishing Inc.
294 Albert Street, Suite 103
Ottawa, Ontario K1P 6E6
E-mail: baico@bellnet.ca
www.baico.ca

Printed by Documents Majemta Inc.

ISBN 978-1-926596-71-6

To

Mom and Dad

Whose ideas and inspiration live on

ACKNOWLEDGEMENTS

No work would be complete without first acknowledging with thanks those who assisted in seeing the work through to its finished product. *It Happened in Canada* Book 2 would not have been started without the encouraging response from readers across Canada who enjoyed *It Happened in Canada* Book 1. The first book would not have started without the keen input and excitement stirred in the author's mind by the wonderful stories and fascinating people the author met at her parent's home. Indeed, these books are a labour of love initiated by the author's parents, Norman and Jean Hills. Sadly, both parents are no longer alive to see the finished second book of *It Happened in Canada*.

As in my previous books, I have made use of terms and labels as they were used in the time of the story being told. I only used the words Indian or Eskimo when the story was placed in a time period when these names were acceptable. I am, in no way, showing disrespect by using these names for the people of First Nations and Inuit ancestry.

There are many others who, along the way, offered assistance, encouragement and information to facilitate the writing of these stories. I would like to thank Philip L. Hartling, Reference Archivist, Nova Scotia Archives and Reference Management; Karen Simonson, Reference Archivist, Heritage Division, Provincial Archives of Alberta; the daughters of Dr. Tom and Mena Orford; as well as many others who stories I heard, whose stories I read to make my stories come to life.

A special thank you, once again, to my family, Clive, Margaret and Henry, for their support, their patience in editing the manuscript and their photographic skills.

INTRODUCTION

What makes a great Canadian? It must be something deeper, stronger, more profound than mere fame and fortune. Greatness is not measured in success, but rather in the humble means by which an individual does a job and does it well, sees a need and fulfills it, acts where action is required without being asked. These are the qualities that are so uniquely Canadian.

Joseph Downer was a high school janitor. During World War I, he served his country. He was a shining example of one Canadian, one individual, who stood up for his beliefs and lived an honourable life. Like so many other Canadians, he had a strength in mind, body and character, plus the humility to do a job without seeking glory. The other people in this book reflect similar honourable traits, the same traits that proudly define the true Canadian spirit. Mrs. Mike, Mena Orford and Dr. Tom Orford were pioneers in the North. W.H. MacAskill was a photographer of exemplary images of the sea; Theodor Heintzman built pianos for everyone; Peggy was a legend of a shipwreck survivor; the Beddis family were farmers, the backbone of Canada's livelihood; Blackie was a dog, a hero.

The ten Canadians represented in this book were chosen for their honourable qualities. These Canadians were not famous. Neither were they rich. Their names have not appeared in any history book. Neither were these names well-known beyond their immediate circle of acquaintances. These people define what makes a Canadian: one who serves others, with honour, with dignity, and for no other reason than to just serve.

CONTENTS

Joseph Downer in uniform prior to his going overseas. Author's collection.

CHAPTER ONE

A MAN OF HONOUR

Joseph stood at attention before his commanding officer. He knew how to respect those in command. It was imperative that the lower ranks recognized the chain of command. The lives of so many men depended on this hierarchy. It only took one person to break that chain, to break the trust. Sometimes the break came from the bottom, from the enlisted men who did the dirty work, who paid the price of death and injury. Other times, however, that break came from the top. Too many of the officers in charge were pampered rich boys whose expensive education had led them to a career as a commissioned officer. They were used to bossing around servants. To these gentlemen officers, the enlisted men were no more than servants, fodder for the brutal playing field of a gruesome war.

Only three men stood in the tent, Joseph, Bert and Major Sharpe, the second-in-command of their regiment, the 116th Battalion. The men often joked about their Major's name and his ability to be anything but 'sharp'. Of course, they made sure that they only joked out of earshot of anyone in command. It would not serve them well for one of their superiors to hear them utter a word of disrespect.

There was no thought of disrespect now. Joseph and Bert stood quietly, obediently, with a serious look on their faces. They knew they were in trouble. It had only been a week since Joseph had been given his Sergeant's stripes. He had been proud of those stripes. He knew that he had earned them and that he deserved them. He had worked from the very bottom of the ranks as an enlisted man. The son of a general labourer, Joseph was no rich man's son. He had been pleased to take charge of a group of men with whom he had served in the mucky trenches of France ever since their arrival almost two years ago. He still had to take orders from above, though. Some of those orders rankled him. It was as if the men in charge had little respect or understanding for those men who were sent out to do the dirty work, the dangerous jobs of war. It was his opinion and subsequent interpretation of some of the orders that placed him in trouble, again.

Sharpe sternly looked across his desk at the two men. He was a very domineering man. In stature, he certainly suited his position as commanding officer. How well the men knew that awful fact. Unfortunately, his common sense was often lacking. The men grumbled about Sharpe's leadership skills; but he was the one in charge and they were under oath to obey. Sharpe had just led the men in a very devastating battle, one that took so many lives, not just from their Battalion. It had been a dreadful, mucky attack on the hapless Germans, who, although equally dredged down by the damp and inclement weather, were better armed than the Canadians and anxious to demonstrate their newest weapon, mustard gas.

The Canadian regiments had been sent out of the city of Ypres, ahead of the other allied forces, to recapture Passchendaele Ridge, just east of the city. It had been shear madness. Joseph knew that and so did his men. Joseph, with his new Sergeant's stripes, had argued that his men were ill equipped. Those soldiers who were lucky enough to have a gas mask had one that fit poorly. Not that a gas mask would do much good against mustard gas. The substance seemed to penetrate the very pores of one's skin, burning it mercilessly. Joseph had argued; but he had not disobeyed orders. The end result had been the same, countless lives lost, many men badly injured and suffering the ill effects of the mustard gas. Joseph could still feel the burning sensation in his throat, even though he had worn his gas mask.

"I am disappointed in you men," Sharpe finally announced. "It is unfortunate; but one must maintain order, whether or not you agree with the command. Is that understood?"

"Yes, Sir," Joseph and Bert answered smartly in unison.

"Sergeant Downer," Sharpe addressed Joseph. "I am removing your stripes. You will return to your former duties as Corporal."

"Yes, Sir," Joseph replied, trying to maintain a smart military air to his voice. He was disappointed. He was afraid this would happen; but he could not stand by and let his men suffer without voicing his opinions. He strongly believed that he owed the men that much. Now he would pay the price of his disobedience. He would be a Corporal once again. Nothing to be ashamed of, he reminded himself. A job well done was always a good job, even if one was assigned latrine duty for the remainder of the war. Well, he was fortunate to miss that horrible assignment; but he was assigned kitchen duty for a week.

<u>POSTSCRIPT</u>

Joseph John Downer (1880-1971) was born in England to Thomas Downer (1843-1883) and Susan Ives (1847-1938). He, and his twin sister Beatrice, had six older siblings. Joseph immigrated to Canada, arriving in Montreal with only pennies in his pocket. Never afraid of hard work, Joseph worked his way across Ontario before settling in Galt (now Cambridge) in southwestern Ontario. He married Emily Ann Davis (1882-1934) in 1900 and raised a son, Henry Thomas (1901-1941). Joseph continued to apply himself to whatever work he could find. He joined the 116th Infantry in 1914 and was sent overseas where, for the next four years, he fought in many of the famous battles of the Great War (what we now call the First World War). Joseph was not ashamed of his humble background; nor was he ashamed of his life as a general labourer. He strongly believed in what was right and he objected to many of the orders issued by those officers whose position in the military was nothing more than prestigious training with little battle experience. He was protective of the men in his group and would openly condemn a senseless action on the battlefield. Consequently, Joseph would frequently obtain his Sergeant's strips, only to lose them a few weeks later over a disagreement with his commanding officer. There is also a story that Joseph was awarded a medal for bravery, only to give the medal back to the commanding officer because he felt that one of his fellow soldiers of lesser rank deserved it more than he did. Joseph was a fine example of what defines a Canadian: someone who is hardworking, proud of who he is and what he does, someone who cares about others. His dedication and sense of honour exemplified the very sentiments that gave Canada such an outstanding reputation in the First World War. Joseph Downer was the author's great grandfather, a loving, caring man and a wonderful gardener. The author still enjoys his rhubarb which flourishes in her garden and she likes to boast that the secret to her recipe for rhubarb pie is her great grandfather's rhubarb.

Cover image of the book, "Mrs. Mike".

CHAPTER TWO

MRS. MIKE

Katherine sat beside the window looking out at the majestic, snow-capped coastal mountains that could be seen from just about anywhere in Vancouver. It was quite a site, especially on a day like this when the sky was a crystal clear blue and the sun was shining brightly. The snow caps brought back so many memories, images of life that seemed so long ago. Was it really forty years ago that she, Katherine Mary, a young Irish girl, just barely sixteen, had met and married that handsome Mountie, Mike Flannigan, in Calgary? He was a distinguished member of the Northwest Mounted Police; she was just a girl, still wet behind the ears.

Oh! The love they shared and the adventures they followed through the coldest and most desolate parts of northern British Columbia and Alberta. After moving with her family from Ireland to Boston, Katherine had ventured west to Calgary to visit family and to recover from an illness. The handsome sergeant had literally swept her off her feet. Coming from a sheltered life, she had often dreamed of such a romance. What she had not expected was a romantic honeymoon on the back of a dogsled, sliding across a frozen wilderness! The newlyweds trekked the backwoods and lived in log cabins, nestled in between rugged mountain ranges such as the ones that she looked at now.

Katherine thought back to the many hardships she had suffered in the North. As newlyweds, she and her husband had lost their first home to a forest fire that destroyed most of the community and took many lives, almost theirs as well. Katherine was expecting her first baby at the time. While Mike fought to save as many people as he could and orchestrated a team of men to fight the raging inferno, Katherine had stood shivering in the river with the other women and children. After the fire, Mike had been transferred even further north. Katherine gave birth en route. She remembered the foreboding she felt as she sat in the cart, cuddling her newborn baby on her lap. Her first vision of the new home community was that of a tragic figure of a lone woman visiting the cemetery. Four years later, an owl flew over their house. It was an Indian superstition that an owl flying overhead foreshadowed death. Katherine had two children by then. The diphtheria epidemic that swept through the community took many of her friend's lives as well as the lives of her two children.

Katherine recalled her feeling of utter desolation. She escaped the North to visit her mother in Boston. She thought she wanted all that civilization had to offer. She discovered that what she really needed was in the North: Mike. The simplicity of her northern existence far outweighed the sophistication and snobbery that she found in Boston. In the North, friends were true friends and life could be lived and enjoyed to its fullness.

Katherine sighed. So many memories! Sadly, Mike had died fifteen years ago. He was considerably older than she was and the life of a Mountie in Canada's northern wilderness was a hard life. The children that they had adopted were now fully grown with lives of their own. Katherine had returned south for a brief period before moving to Vancouver. The coastal climate of British Columbia suited her better now that she was older. After years of living a rugged life, her bones ached and she tired quickly. While she was in Los Angeles, two sisters, Benedict and Nancy Freedman, had listened to her stories about the North. They had written a novel, which they called, *Mrs. Mike*. It was the story of her life. She had been hesitant, at first. Who would want to read a story about her life? She had tried to reason with herself. The book was in print. There was a copy of it lying on the table next to her. It was already a best seller. Perhaps Katherine should have written the book herself. After all, it was her story.

She pondered the ideas that washed through her mind. There were so many stories in her family's past, stories that should be written down for future generations to enjoy, stories that could help the next generation understand both their roots and their lives. The future needed to learn from the past. Katherine had been particularly fond of her great aunt. After reading the copy of *Mrs. Mike* sent to her by the Freedman sisters, Katherine had started writing her aunt's story. It was not as easy as she had first thought. It was one thing to have an idea in one's head. It was another thing altogether to put that idea down on paper.

She could do this, she told herself. She came from a long line of Irish storytellers. The Irish certainly had a way of telling a story that captured the listener's interest. She knew that her family stories were worth telling. After all, she had told her story to two ladies, thus inspiring them to write a book about her life. She had heard her aunt's story told many times, about how she fought the justice system in Ireland to save her son from hanging for a murder he did not commit. Mrs. Honora Kelleen was a strong woman in body, mind and spirit. Her name defined her strength and her personality. She was definitely honourable and committed to seeing things done right.

Katherine picked up the pen that she had set beside the pad of paper. She would call her story, "The Faith of Mrs. Kelleen". Yes, that was a good title. It was her aunt's faith that had sustained her through those difficult times when she had to stand alone against an entire community that believed her son was a murderer. Faith, too, had seen Katherine through many a difficult time, when she lost her home to fire and thought that she had also lost her husband, when she had lost her babies to a terrible sickness, when everything around her seemed so terribly bleak and desolate. Katherine shared many traits with her beloved Aunt Honora. Now, she would use the trait she loved best, that of storytelling, to tell her aunt's story.

"To have seen Honora Kelleen on that early spring morning, as she sat in the small rocker beside the hearth," Katherine started to write. "a shawl around her thin shoulders, her head a little to one side and her eyes closed in a light sleep, you might have thought the merest whisper of wind could blow her over, and a heavy wind crush her entirely. But had you thought so, you would have been wrong. True, Honora was a small, slight woman and, though not yet fifty, a little bent from the harsh work she had had to do since her husband, Patrick, had been taken from her so many years before. True, too, her hair was more white than gray and the small hands now resting in her aproned lap were blue veined and delicately shaped. But the palms of those hands were work-hardened, and the spirit within that small body was one of great strength. And no amount of misfortune could swerve her from her purpose if someone she loved were threatened. Events were to prove this."

Katherine sat back and read the opening description of her aunt. She smiled to herself, seeing in her mind's eye the image of Aunt Honora snuggled in her shawl rocking by the hearth. Katherine was satisfied that she had the gift for telling a good story. She would capture the reader and weave a spell of leprechauns and mischievous little people that would keep the reader entranced to the end of the story. Oh yes! Katherine would have to include the little people, both good and bad. What good Irish story did not include the little people? Katherine may have spent most of her life in Canada and fallen in love with her adopted country; but her spirit was still intertwined with the tales of her ancestors, tales that included the little people.

Katherine Mary Flannigan had not been called Mrs. Mike for no reason. She had been proud to bear the name that attached her to the man in the scarlet coat, the man who upheld the law, took care of the community, and administered medical care when there was no one else available to do the task. Indeed, Katherine's heritage gave her the strength, the courage and the creativity not only to survive, but also to blossom in a rugged northern community, isolated from the world outside. What was it that the sisters had quoted her saying? They had written it at the end of her story. She picked up her copy of *Mrs. Mike* and flipped to the last page. She read out loud to herself and to the proud majestic mountains that loomed just beyond her large picture window:

"But when I left Mike, I left myself; I left Katherine Mary the North had made. I was part of Grouard. Sarah had nursed me; I had nursed Randy. Constance had mended my clothes; I had mended James McTavish's plaid. Oh-Be-Joyful had cared for and loved my children, and now it was I who was to care for and love hers. Mike was right: the pattern of a life isn't a straight line; it crosses and re-crosses, drawing in and tying together other lives, as I do when I gather in the ends of my thread to make a knot."

"It's strange," I said, "but love for a place has to grow in you, the same as any other kind of love."

Yes, Katherine thought to herself. That was the love that her Aunt Honora had passed on to her. That was truly a love worth living for.

POSTSCRIPT

Katherine Mary (O'Fallon) Flannigan was born in Ireland in 1891. She moved with her family to Boston, where she lived with her mother and her sisters in an uncle's house which her mother ran as a boarding house. Suffering from pleurisy, a lung condition, her mother decided to send Katherine to stay with her brother, John, who had a ranch several days north of Calgary. It was at her uncle's ranch that Katherine met Sergeant Mike Flannigan of the Northwest Mounted Police in 1907. She was only sixteen; but it was love at first sight. She married Sergeant Flannigan and followed him north to service the isolated community of Hudson's Hope, over seven hundred miles north of Edmonton and then even further north at Grouard on Great Slave Lake. She endured hardship and loss; but found a great passion for the northern wilderness and its people. A frail girl in Boston, Katherine discovered a renewed vigour and good health in the North. The couple lost both their children; but adopted Indian children. After the Sergeant had passed away, Katherine moved to Vancouver to work during the Second World War, then back to Grouard for a few years. In later years, she lived briefly in Los Angeles, California. It was while she lived in Los Angeles that Katherine told her story to Nancy and Benedict Freedman. Based on her stories, the sisters wrote *Mrs. Mike* in 1947. Katherine moved to Vancouver, where she started writing down her own family stories, including *The Faith of Mrs. Kelleen.*

The Beddis family in front of their recently constructed house on Saltspring Island. B.C. Provincial Archives photo.

The Beddis house as it looks today. Photograph by the author.

CHAPTER THREE

AN ENCOUNTER AT BEDDIS ORCHARDS

"Mother, come quickly!" Delcie called from the front door.

Emily had been working indoors all morning, trying to finish the last of the canning. She and Delcie had been busy the past few days, harvesting the last of the beans and tomatoes. Emily wanted to make sure she canned as much as possible so that the family would not have to depend on others as much this winter as they had the last winter.

The day was quickly warming up and the heat was becoming unbearable in her tiny kitchen as she stood over the boiling pots of tomatoes. She had just finished the last of the beans. She wiped the sweat off her brow with the back of her hand before giving the pot of stewing tomatoes another good stir. The kitchen space was adequate; but she needed more windows. It was dark and, on days like today when she was cooking up a storm, it was stiflingly hot.

She would not complain, though. At least she had a house to call her own. It was much better than the tent that the family had inhabited when first arriving on the shores of Saltspring Island last fall. She had almost feared that she would have to live through the winter in the tent. Fortunately, her husband, the older boys and some of the neighbours were able to fell enough trees and put together a log house before the coldest and dampest part of winter set in. Samuel and the boys continued clearing the land throughout the winter, preparing the space that overlooked the bay to plant a garden in the spring and to start Samuel's dream of an orchard.

"Save the seeds," Samuel had been constantly instructing his children as they bit into the apples that had helped them survive the long journey up the coast from San Francisco.

The Beddis family had emigrated from Bristol England in 1871. That was over ten years ago. They had tried their luck at homesteading in Nebraska. They had been frustrated with their attempts and had moved on to San Francisco. There had been nothing for them in San Francisco, either, so the family, which now consisted of five children, had boarded yet another ship bound for Victoria in British Columbia. Samuel had purchased a sailing sloop in Victoria, loaded his family and the household goods on board, and ventured out to scout the smaller islands that dotted the waters between Vancouver Island and the mainland. A storm had wrecked their sloop, sinking most of the household possessions. The family had survived with very few essentials, including a few apples. Samuel reasoned that these seeds would help them start all over again.

"Will Mother make apple pie with our apples?" Emily remembered Delcie asking her father.

"And applesauce?" Lionel, the youngest son, had added.

"Anything and everything you can think of," Samuel had laughed at his children's comments. They all enjoyed their mother's cooking. The thought of apple pie, even though it might be a few years off before the trees produced enough apples for pie, was enough to make Samuel's mouth water.

They had apple seeds from a large variety of apples. Samuel had reasoned that they could grow a fine orchard with many different apple trees. He planned to graft his apples, once his trees had matured to create his own variety of apple. He had also written home to Bristol, asking his relatives to send slips from their orchards. These had arrived in the late spring with the slips embedded inside Irish potatoes so that they would travel well by mail. Samuel had carefully planted the slips in neat rows. He marked each planting with a stick, instructing the children to take care not to trample the seedlings while playing their games. Emily had quickly planted the potatoes and was pleased to see a large crop growing in her vegetable garden. Samuel had great plans. He planned to eventually add peaches, plums and pears to his orchard and to ship his harvest to Victoria and then to communities north and east. Emily had more simple plans. She planned to take care of her family.

"Mother!" Delcie called, more loudly this time. Her voice sounded both anxious and impatient. She certainly startled Emily out of her reverie with a bit of a jolt. Emily knew that she really must not take time dwelling on the past. There was work to do. Perhaps it was the heat that was getting to her. A breath of fresh air would do her some good.

"Mother!" Delcie called again.

"Coming!" Emily answered. She removed the pot from the heat. She did not want her hard work to burn or, worse, catch fire. Wiping her hands, she walked to the front door. "What is it, Delcie?" she asked her youngest daughter.

"Look!" Delcie pointed towards the garden. "Indians!" she snapped. "They landed on the beach a little while ago. Now they're stealing our food!"

"Oh my!" Emily exclaimed, putting her hands on her cheeks and looking on in dismay. The family had harvested a lot of the produce already. There were still the root crops to dig up. That was what the Indians seemed to be stealing. Not only were they digging up the potatoes and carrots, they were eating them right there before our eyes. "They must be terribly hungry," Emily muttered. She really did not know what to do. She knew that her family needed the produce, too. On the one hand, she did not want to seem uncharitable; but on the other hand, they had so little to see them through the next winter.

Emily and Delcie were alone. Samuel and the boys had left early this morning to help the neighbours cut a path through the thick underbrush of the forest to make a route to Ganges, the main community on Saltspring

Island. It would provide them with a more direct route to the main centre of commerce and trade, much better than the longer route one had to take by boat, traversing around the island. The boys were not expected home until supper time.

Samuel had not seemed overly concerned about leaving his wife and younger daughter alone. The area had seemed so quiet since they had settled there last fall. There had been no sightings of Indians and the locals had reassured them that the few Indians that they did see would be friendly. Now, though, watching her garden being emptied of its contents, Emily was not so sure. She really did not want to cause friction with the Indians. She reasoned that if they were friendly and they were hungry, why not come to the door to ask for some food instead of just stealing it.

Before Emily could think of a reasonable solution, Delcie had run off towards the Indians. "Delcie, come back!" Emily called out in vain. Delcie ignored her mother, continuing on her mission.

"Stop that!" Delcie yelled at the Indians as she approached them. Emily already knew that Delcie had a strong voice. She was forever yelling at her older brothers when she wanted them to do something for her. This voice, however, sounded like it was strong enough to carry as far as Ganges at the top of the island.

"Stop that!" Delcie yelled even louder. She ran up to the leader of the group and gave him a good kick in his shins.

"Oh, no!" Emily groaned. She picked up her skirts and started to run. She saw the leader stand up straight and look sternly down at his opponent. He continued to munch on the carrot that he had pulled from the garden.

"Stop that!" Delcie repeated, giving the leader another kick, then standing rigid with her fists firmly anchored into her sides.

"Oh, no!" Emily groaned again. She came to an abrupt halt halfway between the house and the garden. She held her breath. She did not dare breathe. She stood frozen, pillared to the earth, not knowing what to say or do. She had never seen an Indian before. She had heard stories, though. Most of the stories did not paint a very pleasant picture of them.

Delcie continued to glare at the Indian. No one moved. Even the air seemed to be suddenly still. The leader finished munching on his carrot and threw the tops carelessly aside. Emily gasped as she saw him raise his right hand as a signal to the others. "What now?" she wondered under her breath.

The Indian suddenly broke out into a deep, throaty laugh. He turned to the rest of the group, saying something in their language. They all seemed to turn at once to look at Delcie. They laughed heartily. Delcie just stood there and glared. She did not take kindly to people laughing at her.

The leader motioned towards the bay and the group followed their leader back to the canoes. They laughed as they pushed the canoes into the water. They laughed as they paddled away from the shore.

Emily forced herself to move forward. Delcie remained standing with her hands on her hips. When her mother appeared at her side, Delcie said very softly, "They laughed at me, Mother. They just laughed at me.

Later that evening, Emily related the events to the boys and their father as they ate their supper. Samuel just shook his head. The boys shared a laugh at Delcie's expense.

"They probably thought it was terribly funny that we should send our youngest to defend the family," the oldest snorted.

"And a girl at that," the second oldest added.

"You should be more careful," Samuel scolded his daughter. "This confrontation could have gone terribly wrong. They could have hurt you. They could have kidnapped you."

"But they were stealing our food!" Delcie insisted. "We have to eat, too!"

That evening, tired though he was, Samuel took out his quill and ink and found his notebook. His wife called him a dreamer. He knew that she was right. He enjoyed his dreams and he liked to write about them. His little notebook was his luxury, his way of writing down his thoughts and his dreams, often in verse. As the family settled down for the night, Samuel leaned closer to his notebook so that he could see his writing in the dim light of the single candle that sat on the makeshift table. He had been thinking about this verse all day and now he wanted to write it down before he forgot the words. He wanted to write something profound, something thoughtful, and something that would banish the thoughts that swirled around his mind about his daughter's recent encounter with the Indians. He scratched his quill across the paper of his notebook, trying to remember the words that had floated through his head while he worked.

> *I am looking back, it don't seem long*
> *since wife and I first met*
> *Those happy days when we were young*
> *Sometimes I feel so yet*
> *But ah, I heard the children say*
> *at suppertime tonight*
> *Why, father's hair is getting gray*
> *and Mother's hair is white.*

Samuel could not help but smile at the thought of his wife's hair turning white. After a day like she had just experienced, it was small wonder that her hair should be losing its colour. Delcie's encounter with the Indians was just one of many events that had shaped the family's lives over the past couple of years. He was sure that Emily still suffered nightmares about the night they lost everything on the rough waters between Vancouver Island and the mainland. Indeed they had almost lost their lives! Even though life had presented the Beddis family with countless obstacles, they had persevered and survived. They were hardworking people. They were survivors. Samuel continued to write with a smile etched across his face.

I don't see where the time has gone
since wife and I were wed
Our happiness seemed all our own
and all looked clear ahead
The sun shone out so bright that day
I had no care in life
But now my hair is getting gray
and Mother's hair is white.

POSTSCRIPT

Samuel and Emily Beddis left their home in Bristol England in 1871. After trying their luck at homesteading in Nebraska and working in San Francisco, they moved to Victoria, British Columbia, in 1884 and finally settled on a plot of land on Saltspring Island. With seeds saved from apples eaten on their journey north, Samuel started his orchard. Samuel grafted his own apples and, when the orchard was established, he produced over forty varieties of apples, as well as pears, peaches and plums. He shipped his produce as far north as Yukon. Samuel became a leading figure in the development of the community on Saltspring Island, assisting in the building of the local school and the church. Samuel died in 1893. Emily continued to live in the house her husband had built and his sons continued to run the Beddis orchard.

Theodore August Heintzman, 1907. Photograph by J.H. Beers & Co., Toronto.

THEODOR AND HENRY

"Are you sure you won't stay and help me build the best piano in the world?" Henry asked his friend, Theodor, as the two stood on the platform of Grand Central Station in New York City. They were waiting for the train to arrive, the train that would take Theodor away from the big city, away from the dreams that the two men had shared since they had left their homes in Berlin not so very long ago.

"We were going to make great pianos, weren't we?" Theodor patted his friend fondly on the back. "You will make your pianos in New York," he added. "I shall try my luck in Canada. Toronto is a big city, too. It is growing quickly and there will be a need for pianos. I understand there is plenty of wood in the surrounding forests. Building the pianos in Toronto to sell to the people of Toronto makes good sense. It will be much more economical to buy a piano built locally than it would be to have one shipped from points elsewhere."

"I agree," said Henry, vigorously nodding his head. "But New Yorkers need pianos, too. There are plenty of trees surrounding New York. We can make the best pianos here. There is no need for you to go elsewhere. We have been partners for too long to part now."

Theodor August Heintzman had met Henry E. Steinway at a piano factory in Berlin. They had apprenticed together, learning the trade of building pianos. The growing number of upper middle class families was increasing the desire for a piano in every household, a musical instrument that would add prestige to the family who owned it. There were numerous piano factories all across Europe. Theodor and Henry were very talented craftsmen. They had learned the trade of building pianos. Their goal, however, was to perfect the finished product, not mass produce the item for a quick sale. They had heard of great opportunities in the United States. There were families there who wanted to purchase good quality pianos. Had they not built a number of instruments that had to be crated for shipping overseas? Why not build the piano in the United States and make it more readily available and less expensive?

While Theodor wanted to create fine instruments for everyone, Henry wanted to create a work of art, an instrument that would excel all other instruments. He wanted to create a piano that everyone would envy, one that only the very rich could afford. That was where the men differed in opinion. They both believed in excellence; only Theodor believed that everyone had the right to a fine piano, not just the rich.

"How will you start?" Henry asked his friend.

"I will build them in my kitchen, if I have to," Theodor confessed. "One piano at a time, until I have enough business to find space elsewhere. Then I shall continue

my goal to create the finest grand and upright pianos at the best possible price so as to make it accessible to everyone. Music is not just for the rich and the elite alone. Everyone deserves the right to enjoy music and the best instrument on which to perform it. I will build a quality piano at an affordable price."

Henry shook his head. "I don't know how you'll manage," he confessed. "Building quality pianos at an affordable price may not be quite as simple as you think. Quality is important and that is what will make the Steinway name in pianos."

"As will Heintzman also be a name revered for fine, high quality pianos," Theodor insisted.

"I shall miss you, my friend," Henry said sadly as they both turned at the sound of the train whistle. "I shall miss our arguments as well as our shared knowledge. I wish you well on your venture. Only time will tell which of our pianos becomes the greatest piano ever, the Steinway or the Heintzman."

"The Heintzman, of course," Theodor laughed.

Henry just shook his head. "Perhaps," he claimed. "We shall see. Let history be our judge." Soon Theodor would be boarding his train for Canada and the men would be working solo on their dreams. "We shared a dream. We trained for an art. Now we must go our separate ways."

Theodor nodded. "I wish you well, Henry," he shook his friend's hand fondly. "We have learned from each other. We will both build the best pianos in the world."

"At the very least, we will build the best pianos for our respective countries," Henry agreed. "Farewell Theodor."

"Farewell Henry." Theodor bade his friend good-bye and boarded the train without a backward glance. He had his plans, his dreams and he was off to a new world to start building pianos.

POSTSCRIPT

Theodor August Heintzman was born in Germany in 1817. After training at a piano factory in Berlin, and a brief time spent in New York City, Heintzman immigrated to Canada. There are a number of stories suggesting that Heintzman and Henry E. Steinway (who founded Steinway & Sons pianos) had trained together. Both men developed their own unique, high-quality piano, Steinway in New York City and Heintzman in Toronto. The Heintzman name became synonymous with quality in Canada's piano making industry until well into the twentieth century. The author had the privilege of learning how to play the piano on both a 1930s' Heintzman upright and a late nineteenth-century Heintzman baby grand, the case of which remarkably resembles a similar vintage Steinway.

The author's Heintzman baby grand piano built in the late 1800s.
Photograph by the author.

The lighthouse at Peggy's Cover. Photograph by the author.

CHAPTER FIVE

PEGGY OF THE COVE

Peggy moaned as she slowly rolled over. She was soaking wet and it felt like someone was continually throwing water onto her back. She could feel something gritty in her mouth and she was terribly thirsty. She tried to spit; but her mouth was too dry and nothing came out.

She started to sit up slowly, shading her eyes from the glare of the bright sun that sparkled off the waves crashing over the rocks and splashing Peggy in the face. That explained the repetitive dumping of water on her back. It had been the waves. She looked around her. There was no one, just herself, and the seagulls that screeched as they swooped down onto the rocks and then off into the waters to catch a fish with its beak, which was then brought back to shore to eat. Water seemed to stretch as far as she could see.

Peggy placed her hands on the ground beside her to steady herself. She was feeling a little weak and dizzy. Her fingers brushed over small pebbles and sand. It was a rough, hard surface and not very comfortable for sitting.

Where was she? Nothing looked familiar. She was annoyed with the dry, salty taste in her mouth. She spat again. This time some pieces of fine gravel and pebbles emerged.

"Ugh!" she groaned. She wiped the back of her hand across her mouth.

Her memories were starting to clear. She had been on a big ship with her mother, father and brother. There were lots of other people. Everyone was moving to North America, leaving England to start a new life in the new land. There had been a storm. The ship had rocked precariously back and forth. The waves had viciously swept the decks, washing away everything and everyone in its path, anything that was not well lashed down. Suddenly, there had been a loud snap and the ship had shuddered.

"We are going to drown!" her mother had shrieked. Everyone was screaming. Then, all was silent, except for the storm that raged on. Peggy did not remember anything else.

"Where is everyone?" she cried. "Mother! Father!" she called. Only the seagulls answered with their sorrowful screeches. "Where are you?" She called again and again. The wind swept away her voice while the waves beat a steady rhythm, slapping relentlessly against the rocks and the shoreline.

Peggy stood up carefully, balancing herself with her hands on a large boulder. Her legs felt like the water that had washed her ashore. She continued to look around her. Where could she be? The ship had been too many days at sea for her to be washed ashore in England. She must be somewhere in America.

"Mother! Father!" she called again and again. As her legs steadied, she started to walk along the rocky shoreline, keeping a wary eye on the huge waves that crashed against the rocks.

"Mother! Father!" She continued to call as tears of worry dripped off her cheeks. She stumbled over a large wooden plank. Looking down, she noticed it was rough at the edges. There were sharp objects protruding from the ends. It had obviously been ripped from some large object, perhaps a ship. There were words painted across its length. Peggy squinted to decipher the letters. Mother had taught her how to read; but she was a little slow.

"M.A.R.Y." Peggy read the letters out loud. "R.O.S.E." She thought for a minute. "Mary Rose," she said slowly, sounding out the letters. "It's from the Mary Rose!" She had been on the Mary Rose. Her family had been on it, too. It must have gone down with everyone on board. Was she the only survivor?

Peggy tried to pick up the wooden plank. It was too heavy. She wanted to keep something as a memento. She had nothing else to remind her of the past, to remind her of her family.

"Hello down there!" a voice called from the rocks above. "You had better come up before you are swept away!"

Peggy looked up towards the voice. A man stood at the top of the rocky cliff, waving his hand frantically at her. She laid down her plank. It was too heavy for her to carry up that hill. Hopefully she would find it again. She made her way up the steep incline, mostly crawling as she manoeuvred over boulders and balanced herself from sliding back down in the loose gravel. Everything was slippery from the constant shower of salty water.

"How did you get yourself down there, child?" the kindly old man asked as he grabbed Peggy's hand and pulled her the rest of the way to the top. "I heard the screams in the night and the distinctive cracking of a doomed ship. It must have gone down in the storm. Were you on that ship?"

Peggy nodded. "I don't remember anything after the storm," she mumbled, trying unsuccessfully to blink back her tears. "Have you seen my mother and my father?" she asked him hopefully.

The man shook his head sadly. "No child," he said. "There are no survivors. Only you! What's your name?"

"Peggy," she all but sobbed.

The man took her into his arms and patted her fondly on the back. "There, there," he said soothingly. "Little Peggy of the Cove, you are lucky to be alive. Not many survive a shipwreck off the shores by Halibut Rock. My Mabel and I will raise you as our own. Unless you have family elsewhere."

Peggy shook her head.

"Then you come along with me," he led her along the rocky path away from the cliff. "We shall see if Mabel can help clean you up some and give you something warm to eat."

Peggy followed the kind man to his humble, clapboard cabin, away from the rushing waves of the Atlantic Ocean. Mabel welcomed the girl with open arms. The couple had always wanted children of their own. Now, they had been blessed with a child from the sea, Peggy of the Cove.

POSTSCRIPT

This story is a legend. Peggy's Cove is a tiny fishing village on the eastern point of St. Margaret's Bay along Nova Scotia's south coast. Established as a village in 1811, the legend inspired the tiny community on the cove to be known as Peggy on the Cove. The name attracted tourists and it was fondly shortened to Peggy's Cove. The community has witnessed many disasters from the sea, including Hurricane Juan in 2003, which damaged the cove's breakwater, and Hurricane Bill in 2009, which washed away the remainder of the breakwater, causing extensive flooding in several homes. In 1998, Peggy's Cove made the headlines around the world, this time with a disaster from the skies as Swissair Flight 111 crashed into the ocean near St. Margaret's Bay. A memorial was erected at Peggy's Cove to honour the 229 lives lost in this deadly crash. There are other monuments in Peggy's Cove, memorials to countless lives lost around St. Margaret's Bay, lives lost to the sea.

Wallace Robinson MacAskill with camera on wharf, Halifax waterfront, attributed to Elva B. MacAskill, photographer; NSARM, W.R. MacAskill fonds, 1987-453/3636

CHAPTER SIX

PHOTOGRAPHER OF THE SEA

"Hang on, Wally," one of the deckhands yelled from his perch, strapped to the rigging for safety. Everyone had a nickname onboard *Bluenose*. For Wallace R. MacAskill of St. Peter's on Cape Breton Island, Wally was his nickname. "You'll lose your footing if you're not careful. And your camera, too!"

Wallace was all too familiar with the dangers of the sea. He and his wife, Elva, often ventured out to sea for days on end on his own vessel, *Highlander*. There was nothing he liked better than the rush of adrenaline that coursed through his veins as he manoeuvred his vessel through the ferocious waves of the Atlantic Ocean.

Another cold wave of salty water washed across the deck, soaking everyone and everything in its path. Built in 1921, *Bluenose* was a fine and famous schooner. She was built as a racing and a fishing vessel. With 284 tons displacement and a length of over 160 feet, she was propelled by massive sails. The main mast was 124 feet tall and the foremast was 118 feet. The fine features of this vessel made her quite a sight to behold. It was also quite a task to sail her, requiring a captain, Angus J. Walters of Lunenburg, six officers, a chief cook, and a crew of at least fifteen deckhands. With her able crew, *Bluenose* could handle the most difficult waters of the Atlantic Ocean.

"Sable's off to starboard," the deckhand yelled into the wind. Wallace could barely hear the man. He nodded in understanding. He had hoped to see some of the fabled Sable Island on the return journey from fishing on the Banks. It was not to be. The storm had obscured everything except the huge waves that lashed the ship about like a cork.

"Can't see it now," the deckhand continued. "Don't want to in this weather. Them sandbanks have sunk many a ship in foul weather such as this."

Wallace nodded; but said nothing. He was focusing his camera, aiming for the perfect shot. He was always looking through the lens of a camera, seeking out the right angle, the right lighting, the right pose, the right image. Ever since he had left his hometown of St. Peter's on Cape Breton Island, he had followed his passion, his art. He had studied with some of the finest photographers at the Wade School of Photography in New York City. Pictorialism was the newest craze in art. It was a movement defined by the works of the Photo-Secession Group which included Alfred Stieglitz. These photo-artists pursued the goal of creating impressions on photographic paper, much like the work of the Impressionist painters, William Turner, Edgar Degas, and Claude Monet. Wallace followed their lead and strove to create iconic photographic impressions.

Wallace used his camera to create impressions of the sea, of ships and the men that manned them. After his photograph, *Bluenose*, became a famous image on Canada's 50-cent postage stamp, Captain Walters frequently invited Wallace to join him onboard the schooner. Wherever he went, Wallace took his camera.

As the deckhands manned their stations in this wicked weather, Wallace held tightly to his camera. He wanted to capture the deck of the Bluenose as it heeled from the winds and was washed with a mad gush of vicious waves. He wanted to capture the men as they struggled to keep their balance on a soaked and slippery deck. He wanted to portray the men hard at work, trying to keep the schooner from overturning in these great waves.

Wallace described himself as an artist, much like William Turner, the great English artist who created Impressionistic paintings of life on the sea. Turner had an urge to fully experience the sometimes wild ride across the English Channel. On one trip, Turner actually had himself tied to the mast of a ship. His body tossed and turned with the vessel and he felt the full force of the salt water that splashed across the deck. It was a wild storm, an experience that he later painted.

Wallace did not want to be restricted as Turner had been. He did not want to be tied to a mast, or anything else, for that matter. He wanted his freedom, so that he could move around the schooner with his camera at the ready. Wallace loved the feel and sounds on *Bluenose* as it crested wave after wave and strained with the blow of each wave, some as high as the mast. He was enjoying this wild ride on his favourite schooner. He struggled to keep a grip on his camera, trying to capture the image just right. He knew that the finished picture would be blurry.

It was difficult enough trying to stand and maintain one's balance, let alone hold a camera steady to take a clear picture. The fuzziness would add to the effect, he thought. The viewers of this picture should be able to feel the cold salt water wash their faces. They should feel the chill of the wind and the motion as the schooner rocked from side to side, from wave to wave. It was an impression and a sense of the moment that he was trying to capture, like the Impressionist painters.

Wallace snapped his picture just as *Bluenose* heeled precariously starboard. The waves continued to wash over the deck.

"Watch out!" a deckhand shouted. "Here comes another big one!" His voice was carried away with the wind. Wallace's hands fought to hold onto his camera. His feet struggled to maintain some sense of balance. He was slipping, though. Perhaps it was time to go below deck to ride out the rest of the storm.

"One more shot!" he yelled into the wind. "Just one more shot!" He aimed his camera once again and clicked the shutter.

This was definitely a much wilder ride than he had experienced in a long time. Certainly his outing the other day had been in much calmer waters. He had asked the local High School pipe band to serenade the launch of his own vessel, *Highlander*. He was a highlander with Scottish blood running through his veins, a highlander from the highlands of Cape Breton Island. It was only fitting that he should name his own boat as he had. It was also fitting that he should, later, invite the pipe band to play for his vessel. After the performance, Wallace had welcomed the pipers on board and he had taken them out onto the waters of Halifax Harbour and into the Atlantic Ocean. It had been a foggy day; but the waters were calm and quiet. Wallace suggested that the pipers play during this cruise. He wondered, afterword, what other seamen must have thought as they navigated their vessels through the fog to the sound of some distant bagpipers.

This ride aboard *Bluenose* was far different. Each storm presented its own challenges, its own excitement. Yet, he could hardly wait to return to port, to return to his studio to develop the images that he had taken today. He already knew what he would call the photograph he had just taken: "Starboard Lookout".

POSTSCRIPT

Wallace Robinson MacAskill (1887-1956) was born in the town of St. Peter's on Cape Breton Island in Nova Scotia. Growing up on the narrow strip of land between the Atlantic Ocean and the Bras d'Or Lakes, MacAskill developed a deep love for the sea. He had his own sailboat by the time he was eleven, teaching himself how to sail through the coves of the Bras d'Or. A year later, MacAskill was given a camera as a thank you gift from a tourist he had assisted. This started another passion: photography, particularly photographing life at sea. Wallace left St. Peter's in 1904 to study photography at the Wade School of Photography in New York City. He was influenced by the Pictorialist Movement, led by Alfred Stieglitz, as well as the Impressionist painters, William Turner, Edgar Degas and Claude Monet. In 1907, after he graduated from the Wade School, Wallace returned to St. Peters briefly, then settled in Glace Bay, Nova Scotia, where he set up his own commercial studio and started to establish himself as a marine photographer. He moved to Halifax in 1915, working for Elite Studios owned by Gauvin and Gentzel. It was MacAskill's photographs of the Halifax Explosion and its aftermath that shocked Canadians from coast to coast. By the 1920s, Wallace was starting to receive both national and international recognition. He had established himself as a leading figure in the Pictorialist Movement and his photograph of *Bluenose* under full sail, was used as the image for the 1929 Canadian Bluenose 50-cent postage stamp. The same image was repeated in the 'stamp-on-stamp' issues of 1982 and 1999 postage stamps. It currently appears on the Nova Scotia licence plate and the Canadian dime. MacAskill won several other awards including a bronze medal at the seventh International Sociedad Fotografica in Madrid in 1929. An accomplished sailor, Wallace and *Highlander* won a bronze in the Prince of Wales Cup in 1932-4 and 1938. He continued to promote and publish his photographs in various journals and he put together several books featuring his work, including *Out of Halifax* (1937) and *Lure of the Sea* (1951). The Wallace R. MacAskill collection of photographs is preserved in the Nova Scotia Provincial Archives. The collection contains over four thousand images, plus films, articles, letters and other publications. Wallace's photographs represent one of the foremost collections of marine images in the world.

MacAskill's image of the Bluenose on Canada's 50-cent stamp.

The Newfoundland Dog as it appears on the Newfoundland 14-cent stamp.

CHAPTER SEVEN

THE GENTLE GIANT

"Blackie, come here," Scott called from the back door.

"Where has that dog gone now?" Mother asked from inside the kitchen where she was fussing over the wood stove with the final preparations for the family's supper. "He should be good and hungry by now and at the door begging for his supper."

Scott laughed. "Unless he was too busy begging at our neighbour's door. He certainly has a good appetite."

"He's a big dog," Mother added. "Big dogs come with big appetites."

"He's not that big," Scott defended his best friend. Blackie had been a puppy when he was given to Scott. What better name for a black dog, with thick black fur and deep, dark black eyes that reflected love and compassion! The boy had trained his puppy, teaching him tricks as well as practical things that earned him rewards in good behaviour from his mother. Blackie had been easy to train. He was a Newfoundland dog, not just because he lived in Newfoundland. It was actually the name of the breed. Newfoundland dogs had been on the island since 1610 when colonization had begun. Fishermen quickly discovered that the dog was good to have around for many reasons. It was friendly; it did not take much care; it had a thick warm coat that protected it from the harsh climate; and it made a good rescue dog. There were many tales of sinking seamen who had been saved by their faithful Newfoundland dog. Even Scott and his father felt safer when Blackie was on board their fishing vessel, especially if the seas suddenly became dangerous.

"Blackie," Scott called again from the back door. He turned to his mother. "The snow is coming thick and heavy. It's going to be a bad storm. Father said so. It'll be our first snowfall of the season. I don't want Blackie to get lost out there."

"Your dog is a survivor," his mother reassured him. "If anything, he's probably found someone or something to rescue. A kinder heart I never knew."

Father came running from the cabin at the back where they stored the fishing gear. "Scott! Mother! Come quickly!" he yelled as he ran towards the house. "There's a ship off the banks. I think it's in trouble. I can hear voices, people calling for help."

Mother quickly pushed the pot of stew to the back of the stove where it could stay warm without fear of boiling over or, worse, overflowing and causing a fire. She grabbed her coat and joined Scott at the back door. "Bundle up, Scott!" she instructed her son. "I think I know where you'll find Blackie."

Scott did as he was told and followed his parents across the back of the yard. Father carried a lantern, not that it helped much with the snow flying thick and heavy. The family knew their way well enough to walk blindfolded to the pier where their fishing vessel was tied. It was not the safest thing to do; but there were times when one had to face danger in order to help another. That was the law of those who lived by and with the sea: to always be ready to help. One never knew when one would also be in need of that help.

As they approached the water, the family could hear the cries. There were figures lying on the ground and on the pier itself. Everyone was shivering, coughing and gasping for breath. Scott tried to count; but he could not see everyone. Sure enough, Blackie greeted them at the edge of the pier. He gave a brief bark, wagged his tail and jumped back into the freezing waters.

"That dog saved my life," one man said in a shaky voice. "There must be another fifty out there. We had a full ship." He coughed and wheezed. "Then the storm hit," he continued when he could catch his breath. "All we could see was the snow as it seemed to bounce and reflect off a dark sky and waves as tall as mountains. I thought we were going to die."

"We were tossed into the sea when the ship capsized," another man added in between coughs. "Out of nowhere, this black bundle swam towards us and, one by one, pulled us with his teeth until we had reached the shore. That's some dog you have. I don't know if he'll be able to save everyone; but he's sure trying his hardest."

Mother quickly took charge of the situation. "We can't leave everyone out here," she explained. "Come along,

Scott. While your dog is being the hero at sea, you can help me usher everyone up to the house where it's warm. Then you can run to the neighbours and pass out the cry for help. We will need lots of blankets and warm clothes and more stew than I have on the stove tonight."

While Scott helped his mother direct people up the hill towards their house, Father stood by the pier and helped the remaining survivors ashore as the dog faithfully worked swimming back and forth, dragging one person ashore after another. Everyone was too busy to count how many people Blackie saved that night. The storm raged on for several days. The neighbours divided the survivors amongst them, providing food, clothing and shelter as best they could. It was the way of the Newfoundlanders, hospitality at its best!

It was several days later that the family learned that there had been ninety-two people on board the doomed ship. Blackie had saved every last one of them.

POSTSCRIPT

The Newfoundland dog is a large dog, also fondly nicknamed the Newf, Newfie, The Gentle Giant, and Blackbear. They are a distinctive breed of dog that has its origins with the Vikings who first built settlements in Newfoundland. Since the time of colonization, the Newfoundland dog has been a preferred breed of working dog, especially for fishermen. Very similar to the St. Bernard and the English mastiff; the Newfoundland dog is usually black, but it can also be brown, grey or black and white. It is well known for its kind, caring nature. They make good family pets as they are easy to housebreak. A great swimmer with its strong muscles, water-resistant coat, and webbed feet, the Newfoundland dog is adept at water rescue. In 1900, a doomed ship off the coast of Newfoundland had ninety-two people on board. The actual name and owner of the dog is not known as well as the tale of rescue itself. If it had not been for a certain Newfoundland dog, all ninety-two people on board this doomed ship, caught in a snowstorm, would have drowned. There are numerous other tales of heroic rescues by Newfoundland dogs. For instance, it was a Newfoundland dog that was credited with saving the life of Napoleon Bonaparte in 1815, during his famous escape from exile on the island of Elba.

Bishop Horden Memorial School, Moose Factory.

Dr. Tom Orford in the North. Photograph courtesy of the children of Dr. Tom and Mena Orford.

CHAPTER EIGHT

DR. TOM

"We have turkey," came the voice from the doorway. Tom looked up from his desk to flash a smile at his wife. Mena occasionally popped into his office when she had some news that she wanted to share.

"Some what?" he asked. Tom had been deep in thought trying to compose yet another letter to the government describing the poor living conditions at the residential school in Moose Factory. He had moved his family of three girls to the James Bay community over two years ago. The Orford family had fallen in love with the North and its people during his previous posting, four years spent at a very isolated community hospital on Baffin Island. His efforts to improve the health and well-being of Canada's northern peoples sometimes seemed like fighting an uphill battle. The powers that be, or, in other words, the government officials in Ottawa, could not, or would not, fully appreciate the fact that these people were dying at an alarming rate and quite unnecessarily. It was tuberculosis that was killing them. Tom had done the research. He had conducted the lab tests. He had sent in the reports. He had argued with the officials to send the correct medicine. Tuberculosis could now be treated. He wanted his northern patients to have the same rights to proper medical care as people did in the South. They deserved as much.

Moving to Moose Factory had opened his eyes to yet another government-inflicted wound: the residential schools. Why could the government officials not realize that a child, any child, all children, needed to grow up in their own homes with their own families and not in an institution? The confinement this kind of life imposed upon these young people had medical and psychological repercussions that would carry on well into their adult lives.

"Turkey, dear," Mena repeated, nudging Tom out of his meandering thoughts and memories. He was always full of conflicting emotions whenever he was working on his monthly reports.

"I know you sometimes like to make fun of me," Tom chuckled, shaking his head. "But calling me turkey, in the middle of the work day, no less, is a bit much. Is that all you came over to tell me?"

"Turkey," Mena said yet again. "And I'm not calling you names, dear! You remember last year, you were so disgusted to discover that the children at the residential school were fed bologna and canned beans on Christmas day. You vowed then and there that you would somehow manage to get them a turkey dinner for the next Christmas. Well, my dear, you have succeeded. The turkeys have arrived. Several of them, in fact. Frozen solid; but ready to thaw and cook."

Tom brightened. "Really?" he exclaimed. "That is wonderful news. I was beginning to despair that I would not be able to stand up to my promise. We'll have to organize the women in the community to cook the turkeys. How many did you say?"

"Six, I think," Mena answered.

"Excellent," Tom stated. "We'll see if some of the nurses can help, one turkey apiece. Then we'll take them all up to the school and carve them there. The children will be thrilled. I'm thrilled. A real Christmas dinner!"

"They deserve at least that," Mena agreed. "Especially since they can't go home to be with their families for the holidays."

"I don't agree with these schools, Mena," Tom shook his head. "I know you don't agree either. It's not right to forcefully take children from their homes and shut them up in a school for ten months of the year. I don't understand what made the government think that they could just go into a person's home and take the children away for schooling."

Mena nodded with understanding. They had discussed this issue many times. Tom had even argued with the government officials; but there was nothing he or anyone else could do. It was the law. "Well, dear," she tried to sound positive. "You and I have both done what we could to help make the situation a little better. Now, we need to recruit turkey cooks and start thawing all of these birds so that the children can enjoy their Christmas treat."

"Complete with cranberries and stuffing," Tom added.

"Definitely," Mena agreed. "We had a big case of tinned cranberries sent up with our supplies this year. There will be no shortage of cranberry sauce to go around with the turkey."

"Careful," Tom advised. "You're starting to make me hungry, just thinking about it."

"Wait until you smell the turkey cooking," she laughed. "There are gifts, too. I helped the women in the community knit hats and scarves. We have them all wrapped up. There's one for each child."

"Plus a small toy," Tom reminded her. "Don't forget the box full of toys that came on the supply ship last summer. We had ordered those toys after last Christmas when there had been nothing for the children." He sighed. "I just wish we could do more."

"Like send them all home for Christmas," Mena suggested.

Tom nodded. "Yes," he said. "Like send them all home for Christmas and let them live at home while they attend school."

"Perhaps you ask too much, Tom," Mena scolded her husband fondly.

"Never," he chuckled. "It is not too much to ask that a child is allowed to grow up in his or her own home."

POSTSCRIPT

The Ontario born Dr. Thomas Orford (1908-1981) spent his life fighting the ravages of tuberculosis among Canada's aboriginal people. A 1932 graduate from Queen's University medical school, Dr. Orford helped pioneer the use of streptomycin in the treatment of this disease. Fluent in Inuit, Dr. Orford claimed to have learned patience from the Indians and tolerance from the Inuit. In 1936, he was the second medical officer to be posted to the isolated community of Pangnirtung on Baffin Island, taking with him his wife, Mena, and their two daughters (a third daughter was born while they were up north). In his first year alone, he travelled over 2,200 kilometers, mostly on foot, to treat patients and to teach preventative medicine. He then served in Moose Factory, Edmonton and North Battleford. In 1947, he was appointed by the federal government to be the tuberculosis control officer for Alberta and the Northwest Territories.

Mena Orford in the far north with her husband, Tom, and two of her children. Photograph courtesy of the children of Dr. Tom and Mena Orford.

Mena Orford in the far north. Photograph courtesy of the children of Dr. Tom and Mena Orford.

CHAPTER NINE

NORTHERN TALES

Mena looked over the top of her typewriter at the swirling snow outside her window. How very different were these Edmonton winters! Or were they different? Certainly the temperatures here could drop as low as they often did on Baffin Island. The snow could cause white-outs that would lose even the sanest of persons, just as it did up north. At least, though, the Edmonton winters were relatively shorter than those up north.

It seemed like only yesterday that she and her husband, Tom, had ventured north with their two, very young daughters. They stayed in the tiny, isolated community of Pangnirtung, up the north-eastern coast of Baffin Island. Tom was a doctor. He had signed up for a two-year contract with the government and the family ended up staying for four years. A third daughter was born while they were in the Arctic.

It was a scary adventure at first, Mena recalled; but she quickly fell under the spell of the Arctic and its people. Her parents had been shocked when she married a doctor. In the 1930s, doctors did not earn very much and their pay was often in eggs and chickens. She chuckled as she remembered her first thought upon arriving in the North. She was delighted to learn that she would not have to eat fresh chicken and fresh eggs quite so often. It just took her one winter of canned foods to crave for fresh chicken and fresh eggs.

Mena's mother was doubly shocked when she learned that her daughter was following her husband to Canada's far north. They may as well be going to another planet! The far north in the 1930s was a rugged, isolated land, a land for pioneers, the young at heart and those with an adventurous spirit. There was no way of contacting her daughter once she was up north. The only mail in and out of the community arrived with the supply ship, once a year. She instructed Mena to keep a journal and to write lengthy, newsy letters regularly to bundle up and send out with the supply ship when it arrived in the summer.

Mena tried to keep a journal. She tried to write regularly. Somehow life in the North caught her up in a spell and would not let go. She lived each day to its fullest and, in spite of having help in the house and help with the children, she never did find the time to sit down and just write. The supply ship would arrive and she would be frantically writing late into the night after it was sighted in order to have a letter ready to send out to her family.

Mena had promised herself that she would write her stories about the North once she had settled in the south again. They had not settled in the south for long, when Tom took up a calling to serve at another isolated northern community, Moose Factory. After this posting, Tom was assigned a government position in Edmonton. While Tom was busy at the office, the young people now grown and with families of their own, Mena quickly signed up for a writing course in the hopes that it would inspire her to write her stories. It did! She had just finished typing her last page!

"Two hundred pages!" she exclaimed to herself. "It took two hundred pages and I'm quite sure I've left out several stories." She pulled the last page out of the typewriter and placed it on top of the other pages, then turned the bundle around so that the title page was on top. "Journey North," she looked at her title with satisfaction. It was quite a journey. She turned the page. "Baffin Island," she read out loud to herself. There was no one home. Her husband was at work, leaving her alone to work on her writing. While the storm raged outside, she read the poem that she had written for the frontispiece:

Desert of ice, of mystic solitude
Whence none return that once intrude
Or raise the veil to see behind.

Who gaze upon the violent beauty of your face
Are lost
And must forever wander
Blind.

She had written that poem, and several others, for her writing class. It suited, she thought. It suited her first impressions of the island that was to become her home for four years. It suited this northern attraction that captured her heart and soul, and, even today, called to her. She continued to read the first chapter, "The People". She had given each chapter a name, something that suggested the theme of the stories that particular chapter held. Mena believed that it was the people that attracted her first, and then the land.

They were a primitive, isolated group who called themselves "Kingnaitmiut" (The People Who Live Among Many Mountains).

Where they sprang from I do not know, for I am not a scholar.

But often, as I looked upon the beauty of their barren land, I liked to think that God had put them there, first sweeping it free of all that rots the shining fabric of a human soul.

A place where He could look, when weary of Creation's sorry mess and turn again, refreshed.

For they were a People without guile.

They were a simple people, Mena recalled. They did not judge others and they expected the same from others. Theirs was a life of survival. They hunted to survive. They worked together to survive. They looked after each other to survive. They worried about the cares of the day and not the tomorrows that may or may not come.

Mena picked up her red pencil and started to make some editorial corrections. She had been so intent on her work that she had made countless spelling errors and typographical errors as well. The errors seemed to jump off the page at her. She would have to be diligent in her corrections. She wanted everything to be perfect. She always wanted things to be perfect, though they seldom were. She read to herself and she read out loud, marking as she went along. As she read she felt transported back in time and she relived the first impressions of her new home on Baffin Island as she looked at it from the deck of the supply ship that had carried them north.

"There's the settlement of Panuk now," someone said, and like everyone else, I turned around.

A wide, half-moon segment of flat, dun-coloured barren land spread like an apron from the base of a sheer cliff down to the sea. On it huddled handful of small buildings, as if seeking protection from the lowering heights behind.

It was the most desolate sight I had ever seen in my life.

Mena continued with her editing, losing track of the time. Tom returned home from work. Mena looked up at him in surprise. She had not realized it was so late in the afternoon. She had been so wrapped up in her editing that she had not noticed the fading light outside. She was about half-way through the manuscript.

"Done?" he asked.

"Hmmm!" Mena answered non-syllabically.

"How many pages?" he asked as he shrugged off his winter coat.

"Two hundred," Mena finished the page she was reading and looked up at her husband.

"That's pretty impressive," Tom remarked. "You just started writing about six weeks ago, didn't you?"

Mena thought for a minute. "Yes," she replied. "I guess it has been only six weeks. I feel like I've been away up north again, for another four years."

Tom laughed. "It would feel like that," he agreed. "You've been pretty intent on your writing."

"Hmmm!" Mena shrugged. She looked at her husband fondly. "Do you want to read it?" she asked. "I could use another critical eye."

"Sure," he said as he hung up his coat. He came over and accepted the stack of papers that she had just finished proofing. He grabbed a red pencil, and sat in his comfortable chair to start reading. Mena carried on from where she had left off. The couple read in silence for several hours.

Tom was the first to break the silence. "Wow!" he said, putting down the pages and the pencil, and then standing up to stretch. "That's quite a story. I hadn't realized how frightened you were when we first arrived in Pangnirtung. I was so wrapped up in my work, and in my patients. I was so worried about their lungs, how they would get so sick after the supply ship left each year and then many of them would die."

"You always were dedicated to your work," Mena admitted. "That's how you were able to help so many people. If you hadn't determined the underlying condition that caused these outbreaks and deaths, many more would have died."

"Tuberculosis," Tom recalled. "So many Eskimos suffered from tuberculosis. Who would have thought that tuberculosis would be the root of the problem, in a land where it was always so cold and so dry?"

"Once your tests proved your theory," Mena continued. "You were able to administer the correct drug and treat the real problem that was killing so many Eskimos. You did good work, Tom. You should be proud of what you accomplished and what you did for your patients."

Tom nodded. "I don't know if it's pride I should feel," he admitted. "But I do feel a certain amount of contentment. I'm glad you've written your story, Mena. You always were a good storyteller. Now our descendents, and others, will learn about our life and work in the North. Will you publish it?"

"I think so," Mena said thoughtfully. "I have changed the children's names as well as the names of the others that we knew. I think it's a story that should be shared with all Canadians. We did good work up north and we experienced something that few people could even imagine. It's a story worth telling, worth sharing."

"I agree," said Tom. "I agree."

POSTSCRIPT

Philomena (Mena) Annette Orford was born in Paisley, Scotland in 1907. She immigrated to Canada with her family in 1925 and married Thomas Orford. After Thomas's graduation from Queen's University medical school in 1932, he set up practise in Markham, Ontario. From 1936-1940, the couple lived in Pangnirtung, where Thomas was the only doctor serving in the most isolated hospital in Canada's far north. Mena looked after her two daughters (a third arrived while they were up there) and learned to love everything about the North. In 1940, the family left Pangnirtung for other postings, first at Moose Factory, then in Edmonton and North Battleford. They retired to Edmonton and, after Thomas died in 1981, Mena settled in Killam, Alberta. In 1957, Mena Orford published her book, "Journey North". It won the Alberta I.O.D.E. prize for literature.

Cover image of Mena Orford's book, Journey North.

Mr. Westby surveying the wasteland which would become the famous Sunken Gardens. B.C. Provincial Archives photo.

CHAPTER TEN

WESTBY'S GARDENS

"Mr. Westby," Jenny Butchart held out her hand in greeting.

William Westby took the proffered hand in his strong calloused one. "Very nice to meet you, Mrs. Butchart," he bowed his head slightly in greeting.

"How good of you to meet with me!" Mrs. Butchart claimed. "I have heard wonderful things about your talent in the garden. I understand that you were the head gardener at Renishaw Hall."

"Yes, Ma'am," William replied.

"We met the Selfridges when we visited England a few years ago," Mrs. Butchart offered. "We were invited for tea at their estate. The gardens were truly magnificent. What brought you to Victoria? You had a very prestigious position at Renishaw Hall."

"Yes, I did, Ma'am," William replied. "My son, Bill, was always sick, though. The doctors advised a dryer climate. I brought the family to Canada. We stayed a year in Winnipeg and decided that it was much too cold. Then we moved out here where I tried to start a nursery."

"Yes, I understand that was not very successful," Mrs. Butchart commented. "However, with your references, I am sure you are the right man for the job. I want to create a garden like no other. Come," she motioned to William to follow. "I will show you where I want to build my dream garden."

Mrs. Butchart led William through a grove of trees that surrounded the house. Beyond the trees, there was a sharp drop in the landscape. Everything was barren, littered with rocks and boulders of every size and shape. "My husband's limestone quarry," Mrs. Butchart explained. "Desolate, isn't it?" She sighed. "That is where I want my garden showpiece. I want to reclaim the land and make it a place of beauty. Can you do this for me, Mr. Westby? Can you make something so ugly, so terribly scarred, into a garden paradise?"

William looked down at the cavernous hole. That was the only way he could describe it. The scarred space was large and not very accessible. It would be a monumental task; but what a challenge! It was not something he could possibly turn down. He always loved a challenge. "It would take a long time," he advised Mrs. Butchart. "Considerable manpower and a lot of money."

"Money is no object," Mrs. Butchart claimed. "As for manpower, there is no shortage of men looking for work. I will help, too."

William looked with surprise at the woman who was now his employer. She smiled at him. "Yes," she insisted. "I want to help. It is my garden, after all. You can orchestrate the heavy labour required to move and remove those large rocks and boulders. I don't want everything cleared away. I think we should keep some mementoes to remind us of what this place once was." Looking at the gardener, she asked, "So, what do you think?"

William nodded. "As you wish," he said. "I envision a stone staircase leading down into the dug-out space right about here." William pointed to the left of where they stood surveying the space. "It will connect to a winding stone path that would meander through the gardens over to the far end where we could install a fountain. There should be lots of shrubs around the rock cliff and small plants inserted in the rocky outcrops all along the stone wall. Tall trees at the end of the garden will hide the smokestacks of the factory. We can plant flowering Japanese maple trees along the stone path to make it look very regal and dignified. There will be gardens all around of various flowering plants and manicured lawns in between. We'll rotate the plants depending on the season. Lots of tulips, daffodils, and rhododendrons in the early spring; fuchsias, and begonias for the summer months. How about some roses?"

"No roses," Mrs. Butchart insisted. "I have already started a garden behind the house. That will be my rose sanctuary."

William nodded. "Wildflowers will grace the crevices in the stone wall," he continued. "I will make a list of the flowers that would grow well in this protected space."

"Yes, yes!" Mrs. Butchart clapped her hands in excitement. "I can see that you are definitely the man for the job. When can you start?"

"Today," William nodded in agreement. "I can start right now, if you like."

"Yes, yes," Mrs. Butchart exclaimed. "The sooner the better!"

William parted company with his new employer. He walked down the slope that was once used to roll the carts full of limestone to the top of the quarry where they were transported to the factory beyond. He would keep this slope. It would be useful for dragging out the unwanted rocks and boulders. It would also make it easier to wheel down carts full of good topsoil, peat moss and manure. He would have to bring in loads and loads of dirt to build up a good soil base for his garden. Even the trees would not fare well in this toxic wasteland.

As he walked down the slope, William made notes in his head. He would keep this slope when all was finished. A path, lined with flowering maples and rhododendrons would be a pleasant walk to or from the Sunken Gardens.

Yes! He smiled to himself. That is what they would call his garden masterpiece when it was finished. The Sunken Gardens! Westby's Sunken Gardens! Though he wondered if, in fact, future generations would remember him as the garden's architect. Usually it was the owner, the employer, the one who paid the bills, who stole the glory. More likely the gardens would be known as Jenny's Sunken Gardens, after his employer, Mrs. Jenny Butchart. Or, perhaps the gardens would be world famous as the Butchart Gardens. Already, he had heard people comment about Jenny's gardens, Jenny's dreams.

These gardens would not be his gardens, William chastised himself. Westby would be no more than a name on his employer's records, someone who was paid to do a job. He would have a good job on the Butchart Estate for at least ten years. It would take that long to do the job. He could rest assured of steady work and a steady pay cheque, nothing more, nothing less. That was what he was hired to do, not to seek fame or glory.

He had better start working on Jenny's dream and stop dreaming his own dreams. Life was work. A good job was a job well done and that was all there was to it. His good job would be to make Jenny's dream a reality.

POSTSCRIPT

William Henry Westby was born in Yorkshire, England in 1875. A descendent of a long line of gardeners, he began working as an apprentice gardener at the Duke of Portland's estate, Welbeck Abbey, and was later head gardener at the Selfridges estate, Renishaw Hall. Due to his son's health problems, Westby moved his family to Canada, first settling in Winnipeg and then moving on to Victoria, British Columbia, in 1912. He became the head gardener of the Butchart Estate just outside of Victoria, as well as the chief architect for the sunken gardens, the centrepiece of the world famous attraction known today as the Butchart Gardens. Mrs. (Jenny) Butchart relished in the glory; but behind her dream was a man who had the talent to achieve something of remarkable beauty out of a desolate limestone quarry. W.H. Westby, the forgotten gardener who was the architect of the Butchart's Sunken Garden, died in 1929.

The Sunken Gardens as they appear today. Photograph by the author.

CHAPTER ONE

1. What were some of the famous battles around Ypres in France during the First World War?

2. What happened at Passchendaele Ridge?

3. How many Canadian soldiers lost their lives at Passchendaele Ridge?

4. What was the German's most deadly weapon in this battle?

5. What defence did the Canadians have against this weapon? Was it effective? Why?

6. What city in Canada was the home base of the 116th Battalion?

7. Who was the second-in-command of the 116th Battalion?

8. Why did the men think that Sharpe was not very sharp?

9. What rank was Joseph Downer at the beginning of the story?

10. What happened to Joseph Downer after the battle?

11. Do you think this was fair? Why?

ACTIVITIES

1. Choose someone from your family history or an historic
    Canadian who served in the First World War. Research
    his/her story and write your own story based on this
    person's experiences during the war.

2. On a large scale map of France, locate Ypres. Research
    the First World War battles that took place around the
    city of Ypres and mark these battles on the map. Write a
    story about one of these battles.

CHAPTER TWO

1. How old was Katherine when she first met her husband?

2. What was her full name before she married Mike Flannigan?

3. What type of work did her husband do? What was his rank?

4. Where did this work take Mike and his new bride?

5. Describe some of the hardships Katherine experienced during her married life.

6. How would you feel if you were in Katherine's shoes?

7. How did Katherine's story become well known?

8. Why do you think Katherine didn't write this story herself?

9. Who is Katherine writing about in the story?

10. Why does Katherine feel an affinity with this distant relation of hers?

ACTIVITIES

1. Imagine you are living in the far north in the early 1900s. There are no roads connecting your community to the outside world. There are no trains, airplanes, telephones, radios, television, no video games and no computer. You are completely cut off from the rest of the world except for the once-a-year mail that is delivered to the local Hudson's Bay post. Write a story about your life in this isolated community. Don't forget to be very descriptive.

2. Read *Mrs. Mike*. Pick a scene from the story and write a skit based on that part of the story. As a class, act out the skit.

CHAPTER THREE

1. Why are farmers so important for the survival of any community?

2. What types of hardships would the early pioneer farmers have faced?

3. What hardships did the Beddis family face when they first tried to start their farm on Saltspring Island?

4. How did they survive the first winter?

5. How did they manage to clear a road from their farm to the main community of Ganges?

6. Why was this road so important to the Beddis family?

7. What happened while the men were away working on this road?

8. Why was Emily so frightened of the Indians?

9. Why was Delcie so angry with the Indians?

<u>ACTIVITIES</u>

Find Saltspring Island on a map of Canada. Find a bigger map of the island and see if you can find Beddis Bay and Ganges. Draw a route that the Beddis family might have used when commuting between Beddis Bay and Ganges before the road was built. Draw in a possible route for the road. Can you determine the exact route the road would take? Why or why not? Compare the route that you chose for the road with the one that is actually marked on the map. Why do you think it's different? Make a list of things that need to be considered when constructing a road.

CHAPTER FOUR

1. Who was waiting at the train station with Theodor?

2. How did the two men meet?

3. What did the two men do for a living?

4. Why was Theodor leaving New York City?

5. Where was Theodor going and why did he choose to go there?

6. How did Theodor plan to start his business?

7. What was Theodor's goal?

8. Why did Theodor want to create the best piano at the best price?

<u>ACTIVITIES</u>

Imagine you are a trained piano builder in the middle of the nineteenth-century. You have decided to move to Canada to start your own business building pianos. Make a list of what materials you would need to build a piano and where might be the best place to start this business based on the availability of these materials. What sort of difficulties might you encounter in obtaining these materials, building your pianos and selling/shipping your finished product?

CHAPTER FIVE

1. How was Peggy's Cove named?
2. Who was Peggy of the Cove and how did she acquire this name?
3. What happened to Peggy's family?
4. Who took care of Peggy after the shipwreck?
5. How many disasters have struck the area around St. Margaret's Bay, near Peggy's Cove?
6. Why is the water so dangerous there?
7. What disaster struck the area from the air?

ACTIVITIES

Create a design for a memorial to all those who lost their lives at sea near Peggy's Cove. Remember to include seamen as well as ordinary people. What words would you write on your memorial to commemorate those who lost their lives near Peggy's Cove?

CHAPTER SIX

1. Who was Wallace Robinson MacAskill? Why was he so well known?

2. What famous schooner did he like to photograph?

3. What made this schooner so famous?

4. What happened to one of his photographs of this schooner?

5. What was MacAskill doing on the schooner?

6. Why was it so difficult for him to take his pictures?

7. What type of camera do you think MacAskill used?

ACTIVITIES

Make a Pinhole Camera using the following steps. Take some pictures and develop them in a darkroom setting. Mount your photographs, give them titles and sign them. Hang them in a special place and invite people to attend your Exhibition of Pinhole Photographs. Is it easy to take a clear picture with a Pinhole Camera? Why or why not? Now imagine you are on a schooner like MacAskill and you are experiencing rough weather. Would it be easy to take a clear picture on this schooner?

HOW TO MAKE A PINHOLE CAMERA

Pinhole camera made from a can.

MATERIALS

1 small, light-tight can or box for the camera body about three to six inches in length (like a two-pound coffee can, a clean paint can, a vegetable shortening can, a peanut can or a cylindrical oatmeal box)

black paint

heavy black paper like the package backing of photographic paper OR thin metal like heavy duty aluminum foil

number 10 sewing needle

thick, heavy, dark tape (masking tape or construction tape)

cardboard

3 ¼ by 4 ¼ -inch photographic paper

photographic chemicals for printing the exposed paper (developer, stop, fixer)

DIRECTIONS

1. Paint the can and the lid both inside and out with a dull black paint.

2. Make a ¼ -inch hole at the opposite end of the can from the open end. (It is much easier to load paper/film at the open end than at the closed end.)

3. On heavy black paper or thin metal, make a pinhole about 1/75-inch in diameter by piercing it with a number 10 sewing needle, rotating the needle as you push it through. If you are using aluminum foil, sandwich the foil between two lightweight cards to prevent the foil from bunching or tearing. Securely attach the paper/foil over the large hole.

4. For the shutter, cut a small piece of dark paper (about one-inch by two-inches). Place it over the pinhole, leaving the bottom end loosely taped so that it can be easily folded up to take the picture.

5. For the viewfinder (although not really necessary for a Pinhole Camera), cut a piece of cardboard (about one-inch by two-inches). Pierce a hole about ½-inch from the top of the two-inch length. Place the cardboard on the opposite end of the camera from the shutter, making sure that it is centred and that the peephole is above the camera. Tape securely in place.

6. In order to load the camera, find a room that is completely dark. Using a photographic safelight or a flashlight with the light end securely covered with several layers of red cellophane paper (which must be placed at least six feet away), remove one sheet of

photographic paper from its protective packaging. With the emulsion side of the paper (the shiny side) facing the pinhole, tape the film securely inside the camera at the opposite end of the camera to the pinhole. Close the lid of the camera. Make sure that the shutter is securely taped shut. It is now safe to go out into the light to take a picture.

7. Aim the camera at the subject. Hold the camera steady; gently lift the paper off the shutter and count. Pictures taken in sunlight require an exposure of about two minutes. When you finish counting, securely re-fasten the paper over the shutter. Return to the darkroom and, using only the safelight, process the pictures in the chemicals as directed on the photographic paper package. Once the picture has been fixed, rinse well and hang or lay flat to dry overnight.

CHAPTER SEVEN

1. Who is the hero in this story?

2. What type of dog is he?

3. Why is this breed of dog so popular?

4. How long has this breed of dog been known to exist?

5. From what breed of dog did the Newfoundland dog descend?

6. Why do fishermen prefer the Newfoundland dog to any other breed of dog?

7. Make a list of all the famous people through history who have owned a Newfoundland dog.

<u>ACTIVITIES</u>

1. The Newfoundland dog is a popular family pet as well as a working dog. You have inherited a purebred Newfoundland dog with a very distinctive pedigree and you want to go into business breeding and selling Newfoundland dogs. Design a poster to promote your new business. Make sure your poster promotes the Newfoundland dog as the best dog available.

2. You have always wanted a puppy. Your grandfather gives you one as a Christmas present. This puppy is already big, fluffy and very loveable. The two of you become very attached to each other. One day this puppy saves your life. Write a story describing the rescue.

CHAPTER EIGHT

1. Who was Dr. Tom?

2. Where did he first practice medicine?

3. Why did he accept a posting way up north on Baffin Island?

4. What critical medical condition did he discover with his Inuit patients on Baffin Island?

5. What medicine did Dr. Tom request from the government to treat this medical condition?

6. Where did Dr. Tom practice medicine after he left Baffin Island?

7. What is an Indian Residential School?

8. Why were Dr. Tom and his wife, Mena, so opposed to the Indian Residential Schools?

9. What treat did Dr. Tom arrange for the children at the Indian Residential School in Moose Factory?

<u>ACTIVITIES</u>

You are of First Nations descent, living in the 1940s in northern Canada. The government sends the Royal Canadian Mounted Police to your doorstep and forcefully take you away to an Indian Residential School where you must live and study for the next ten months. You are forced to speak English. You are punished if you are caught speaking your native tongue. You sleep in a dormitory that is cold in the winter and hot and buggy in the warmer weather. You keep a journal of your life and experiences at this school. Write a daily journal entry for at least a week, sharing your experiences at this school.

CHAPTER NINE

1. What book did Mena Orford write?

2. What award did Mena's book receive?

3. How long did it take her to write this book?

4. Whose story was she telling? When and where did this story take place?

5. Why do you think she wrote this story?

6. How do you think Mena felt when she first arrived at Pangnirtung?

7. How do you think she felt when she left Pangnirtung four years later?

<u>ACTIVITIES</u>

Obtain a copy of Mena Orford's book, *Journey North.* Read it together as a class or individually. Write a book report about *Journey North.* Pick a scene from the story and draw a picture to illustrate this scene.

CHAPTER TEN

1. Who was W.H. Wesby?

2. What was he trained to do?

3. Where did he receive his training?

4. Why did he move his family to Victoria?

5. Who is Jenny Butchart?

6. Why is the Butchart name so famous?

7. Why did Jenny receive all of the glory for the Sunken Gardens created and constructed by Westby?

8. How would you feel if someone else took all of the glory for your hard work? Why? Would you be able to do anything about it if you lived in the early part of the twentieth-century?

<u>ACTIVITIES</u>

Create a live model of a sunken garden using found materials and real plants. OR, create a garden window box using found materials and real plants. OR, find a desolate place that needs cleaning up and beautifying. Make it your class or individual project to create a garden design in this space.

Cooper, Dorothy. *MacAskill: Seascapes and Sailing Ships.* Halifax: Nimbus, 1987.

Flannigan, Katherine Mary. *The Faith of Mrs. Kelleen.* New York: Coward-McCann, 1951.

Freedman, Benedict and Nancy. *Mrs. Mike: the Story of Katherine Mary Flannigan.* Toronto: Longmans, Green, 1947.

"Heintzman & Co.", http://en.wikipedia.org/wiki/Heintzman_%26_Co

Hill, Beth, et. al. *Times Past: Salt Spring Island Houses and History Before the Turn of the Century.* Saltspring Island: Community Arts Council, 1983.

"Katherine Mary Flannigan", http://en.wikipedia.org/wiki/Katherine_Mary_Flannigan

"Newfoundland (dog)", http://en.wikipedia.org/wiki/Newfoundland_(dog)

Nova Scotia Archives & Records Management. "W.R. MacAskill", http://www.gov.ns.ca/nsarm/virtual/macaskill/essay.asp?Language=English

Orford, Emily-Jane, "The Beddis Family", *Western People.* July 16, 1992, p. 8.

Orford, Emily-Jane, "W.H. Westby: Forgotten Gardener Who Created Butchart's Showcase", *The Islander.* April 24, 1988.

"Orford, Philomena (Mena) Annette", *Edmonton Journal*. November 10, 1996.

"Peggy's Cove", http://en.wikipedia.org/wiki/Peggys_ Cove,_Nova_Scotia

"Philomena (Mena) Orford", *The Pleasant County: Killam and District, 1903-1993*. Killam: 1994.